Dan
AND THE MISCHIEF
Boy

TRUE
STORIES OF
AN AFRICAN
FAMILY

PAUL VALLELY

PICTURES BY MIKE GOLDWATER

Fount
An Imprint of HarperCollinsPublishers

Christian Aid

For Catherine

Paul Vallely and Mike Goldwater went to visit Daniel and his family in Eritrea and stayed with them for three weeks. Paul lives in London and is a writer for the *Daily Telegraph* newspaper. *Daniel and the Mischief Boy* is his fifth book. Mike Goldwater is an award-winning photographer based in London. This is his third book.

Thanks to Victoria, Thomas, Laura, Sam, and Celia who read these stories and made useful suggestions. Thanks to Ben for drawing the map. Thanks to Gebru Tesfa-Mariam for advice on details of life in Eritrea. And very special thanks to Christian Aid who organised our journey to Eritrea.

This book has been published in co-operation with Christian Aid, which helps people like Daniel and his family to grow food and look after themselves and, if the crops fail, sends food trucks to help keep families alive.

Fount Paperbacks is an Imprint of
HarperCollins*Religious*
Part of HarperCollins*Publishers*
77–85 Fulham Palace Road, London W6 8JB

First published in Great Britain
in 1993 by Fount Paperbacks
1 3 5 7 9 8 6 4 2

A catalogue record for this book is
available from the British Library

ISBN 0 00 627675 X

Printed and bound in Great Britain by
Scotprint Limited, Musselburgh, Edinburgh

CONTENTS

Chapter One

How Kudos nearly drowned the ox

page 6

Chapter Two

Azmera has an adventure

page 19

Chapter Three

Daniel's midnight journey

page 30

Chapter Four

The dozy donkey disaster

page 40

Daniel   Mother   Father   Azmera Kudos Mabret
                     Baby   Teklom

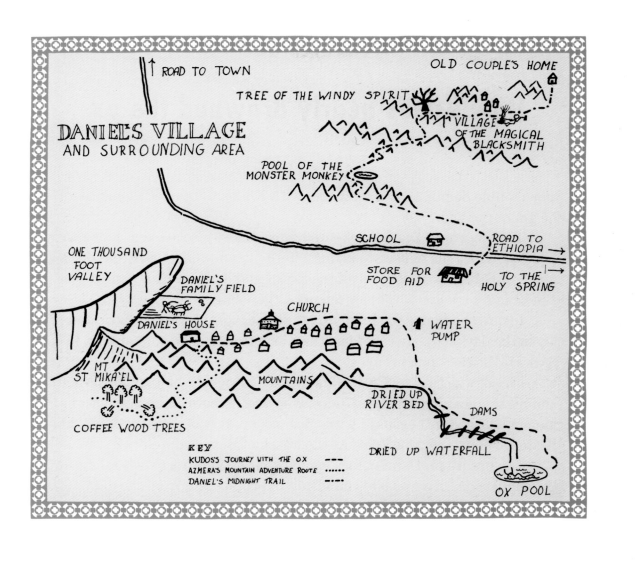

CHAPTER ONE

How Kudos nearly drowned the ox

The trouble began, as it usually did, with Kudos. It started even before he got out of bed.

That morning Daniel woke up before the sun rose over the rocky plain on which his house stood, high in the mountains of Eritrea to the north of Ethiopia. It was one of the driest and dustiest places in Africa. But at night a layer of cold air fell upon the village.

Inside the house made of stones stuck together with mud Daniel lay in the darkness. He could feel the warm breath of an animal upon his face. He did not open his eyes.

Daniel was twelve. Beside him in the old rickety bed lay his father and his ten year old brother, Kudos, who was being well-behaved at the moment. That was because he was fast asleep. It was the only time that Kudos, whom everyone knew as the Mischief Boy, was well-behaved.

The breath on Daniel's face came from the family's ox who slept in the same room. He was allowed inside to protect him from the damp of the winter night. The ox was named Senay, which meant Good News. But Kudos, of course, just called him Smelly.

There were only two rooms in the family's little house. In the other room Daniel's mother slept on a big bed, also made from baked mud, which was built into the side of the house. With her slept the baby, his sisters and their younger brother, Teklom. He was only two so he was still allowed to sleep next door with his mother and the girls.

In the other room Mother was already up and beginning the day's housework. Daniel's sister Mabret was up too. She was only eight but, without being asked, she began her first job of the day, sweeping the floor to clear up the mess the family's hen and its six chicks had made in the night.

Teklom and his other sister, Azmera, were still in bed but they were awake. They lay snug and warm amid the blankets and watched their sister hard at work.

Azmera, who was six, lay on her tummy and yawned.

"You've missed a bit," she said, cheekily. Mabret pulled a face in reply and carried on sweeping.

Teklom crawled out of bed and waddled out into the boys' room next door. His father was already up, washing in the yard, but his two big brothers were still in bed.

The toddler made an announcement in his loudest voice.

"Teklom not sleeping with girls any more," he said.

Daniel swung his legs over the side of the bed. He did not need to dress; like all his family he only had one set of clothes. He had worn them for more than two years. In Eritrea it had not rained for that long. The ground was dry and the streams were empty. There was no water to wash them. It didn't matter, his mother sometimes joked, because washing only wore out clothes more quickly. Instead, Daniel washed his face with water from a little tin.

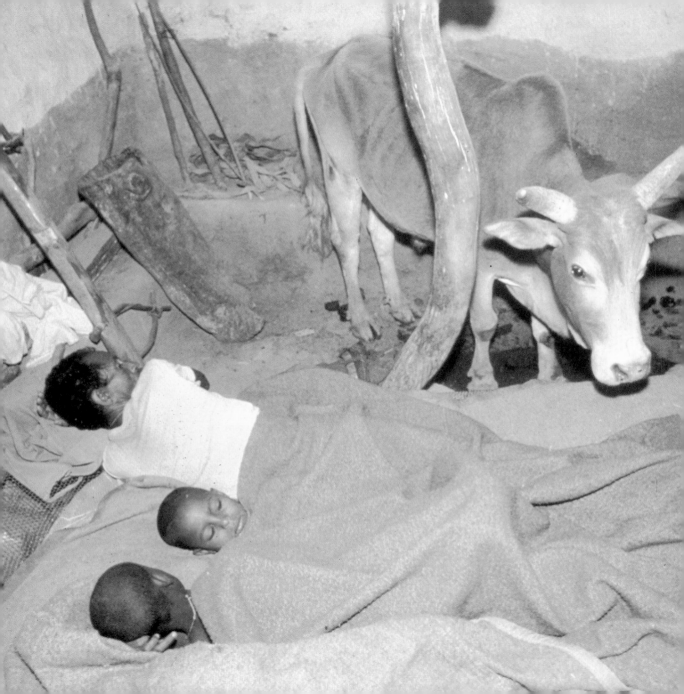

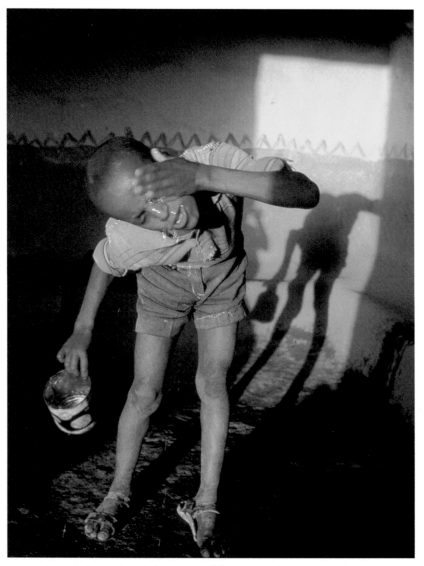

Daniel washes his face with water from a little tin

"Teklom not sleeping with girls any more," the little boy said again and waited for a response.

"Oh really," said Daniel, with a yawn.

In the bed Kudos was pretending still to be asleep, huddled lazily inside the old grey blanket on top of the goatskins on which they slept. He opened one eye and peered out at his little brother. Teklom said the same thing every morning. And every night he changed his mind and cried to stay with his mother and the girls.

Teklom wandered over to the bed and began to tug at the old grey blanket.

"Go away," said Kudos in a grumpy voice. Teklom pulled the blanket off his brother and then fell down on his bottom with a bump. The blanket fell on top of him, making him look like a little grey mountain.

"There's no room in here for you, you little pest," said Kudos, sitting up crossly. "Tonight you'll have to go and sleep with the donkey outside in the dark."

From underneath the blanket Teklom howled.

Just then their father came back. He was not amused. He lifted the cover from his little boy and picked Teklom up for a cuddle.

"You big bully," he said to Kudos. "If you can't live in peace with your little brother then get out of the house. Take the ox down to the waterhole for a drink. Go on. Off with you."

Kudos got out of bed in a sulk and stomped out of the house. He picked up a stick from the yard and set off down the path through the village, prodding the poor old ox with the stick as he walked.

The family's home was on the edge of the group of houses which stood in a crooked line where the high rocky plain met the steep mountain behind the village. The ox had made the journey many times before and knew the way. He picked his way slowly along the stony path. Kudos plodded grumpily along behind.

He had not gone far when he heard a voice coming from a house further up the slope.

"Kudos! Where are you going?"

He looked up and saw a curly-haired boy with a big grin. It was his friend Samson.

"To take the ox for water," Kudos said.

"It's a bit early, isn't it?"

"I wanted to get going before the sun came up and it got too hot," lied Kudos. He did not want his friend to know that he had been sent off in disgrace. Already he was starting to feel ashamed of himself for being snappy with his little brother.

"Okay, wait for me. I'll go and get ours and we can go together," said Samson.

A minute later he was back with another ox. Samson's mother came to the wall above them.

"Take the donkey too," she shouted.

"No fear!" replied Samson.

The two boys set off again, this time with two oxen. But as they were passing the church on the little hill in the middle of the village, Kudos heard another voice. It was his aunt, who lived near there.

"Hey Kudos! Take my ox too."

A few yards later they added another animal. This one was from a friend of Samson's father. Then they were joined by three other boys,

Samson and Kudos
head for the waterhole

each with a group of oxen of his own. By the time they left the village the five boys were herding thirty oxen. But they took no donkeys. Every time one of the women asked them to they said: "Not likely!"

"An ox is a pretty stupid creature," said Kudos to his friend. "But an ox is not so stupid as a donkey."

"Donkeys are dumb," agreed Samson. "You can bet that if we had agreed to take one it would have fallen in the waterhole and drowned."

That was exactly what had happened to a donkey from the village only the week before. The boy in charge of it had got into serious trouble. Kudos and Samson did not want the same thing to happen to them.

It was a long way to the waterhole. It took almost two hours of steady walking to reach it. It was not the nearest water to the village. At the bottom of the hill, between the village and the road into town, there was an old metal pump. But because there had been no rain for two years there was not much for the pump to bring up. Even if you heaved on its handle very hard it produced only a trickle of water. There was barely enough for people to drink and certainly not enough for an ox. So the boys turned to the right and followed the track of a dry river bed for another hour.

It was not a boring walk that day. Samson had a new catapult. It was made from a stout piece of wood and the rubber from inside an old bicycle tyre. His uncle had brought the rubber back from a visit to the town, three hours walk away. The five boys took it in turn to see how far they could fire the stones which covered the fields all around. Each boy was allowed to fire six shots before passing the catapult on.

As they walked they passed seven dams in the river bed. Each one had been built by the villagers to hold back some of the river's water when the rains came. But each one was now dry.

At the eighth dam, however, there was water. The dam was at the base of a dried up old waterfall. Kudos and Samson stood on the edge and looked over. Down below, about thirty feet beneath them, was a murky brown pool. It was the colour of milky coffee.

They walked down the steep path that led to the bottom. Around the pool were a group of children who had come from villages nearby. With them they had a crowd of about fifty oxen.

"Oh no," said Samson. "They'll be ages. We might as well wait up there." They turned around and climbed back up to the top.

"My turn with the catapult," said Kudos.

He sat down on the slab of hard rock at the edge of the waterfall. All around in hollows in the rock were smooth little pebbles which had collected there in the days before the river dried out.

"Great," said Kudos. "These will be perfect."

He fitted one into the catapult and pulled back the elastic. Twang! The round little stone shot high into the air.

"Brilliant," said Samson. "Let me have a go."

But Kudos had five more shots. Taking his time he searched for five perfect pebbles.

What he did not notice was that the ox was on the move.

Senay the ox may not have been thirsty when he set out for the waterhole. But he had walked for almost two hours and the sun was climbing higher in the sky. He was hot and saw no reason why he should wait at the top when water was only a few yards away.

The ox began to lollop down the steep track to the pool.

But Kudos saw nothing. He fitted the next of the perfect pebbles into the sling and fired it in a soaring arc into the sky. It hit the ground with a click just as the ox hit the water with a mighty splash.

Senay had rushed greedily at the water. But the mud at the edge of the pool was soft and slippery from the many feet of the other animals. The ox slid suddenly in. Spladoosh!

Up at the top the boys turned round. Kudos felt his heart leap up to his mouth when he saw what had happened.

"Oh no! It's Smelly. He's fallen in."

Kudos stuffed the catapult in his pocket. Then he slithered down the path and landed at the bottom in a cloud of dust.

In the pool the ox began to swim desperately round in circles. Kudos splashed to the edge and began to shout in a mad fury. But the ox ignored him and continued to swim round and round.

Ten times the ox circled. And each time he went slower and slower.

"We've got to get him out," shouted Samson. "When he stops he will just go under."

"Take my hand," said Kudos. Clinging on to Samson's arm he edged slowly out into the water.

Kudos was afraid. If he fell in he might drown too. He could not swim. None of the children in the village could swim. It had rained so little in recent years that there had been nowhere for them to learn.

In his other hand Kudos waved his stick.

"This way," he shouted to the ox. "This is the easiest place to get out."

But the animal took no notice of his wild waving. He just went

round and round, with a look of alarm on his face. Kudos began to feel his feet slipping.

"Pull me back," he said. "I've had an idea."

Safe away from the edge Kudos threw down his stick. He pulled the catapult from his pocket. From his other pocket he took the remaining four perfect pebbles.

He fitted the first one and fired it. It hit the water just in front of the ox. A look of panic came onto the face of the animal. He splashed around and changed direction. But he was still not heading the right way.

Kudos fired the second. Senay changed again. But he was still swimming away from the safe exit.

Kudos fired the third pebble. And still no luck.

He slipped the last perfect pebble into the sling. He took a deep breath and aimed carefully. Ping! It hit the water just a few inches in front of the ox's nose.

A great moo came from Senay's lips. He swivelled round in fright. At last he began to move in the right direction. He was heading for the safe way out. Two minutes later he clambered out and stood, shaking with exhaustion, at the side of the pool.

"Great shot," said Samson.

Kudos jumped in the air with joy. But as he landed both his feet slipped in the slimy mud. He fell backwards and landed on his bottom, just as Teklom had done at the start of the day. And the two friends burst out laughing.

CHAPTER TWO

Azmera has an adventure

Azmera was not like Kudos. It was not what she *did* that got her into trouble. It was what she *said*. Azmera was the cheeky one. Everyone in the village knew that. Whenever Daniel's little sister was asked to do something she always had a naughty reply.

If her mother asked her to get something from the little kitchen next to the house she would say: "It's not my turn. Ask Kudos."

If her mother asked her to fetch some water from their big storage jar she would say: "I'm not tall enough. Ask Daniel."

If her mother asked her to play with Teklom to stop him getting into mischief she would say: "No-one can keep *him* out of trouble."

Mother's reply was always the same. "Go on. Don't be cheeky. Just do it," she said. And Azmera always did it, with another grumble.

That week her sister Terhas was away. Terhas was fifteen. She had not been well. She had dizzy fits and fever. So she was sent to drink from the waters of a holy spring. It could cure any disease, she was told. She had set out on a three-day walk over the mountains to get there.

While she was away Mabret, who was eight, proudly took over her big sister's jobs.

"Now I am the oldest girl in the house," she said. "I will help mother." And Mabret became busy all day, sweeping the floor, lighting the fire, washing the pots, minding the baby and watering the five little trees which the family was growing on the hillside nearby.

Azmera was only two years younger and she thought that Mabret was getting too big for her boots. She lay in bed with the baby and teased her, calling her Little Mother.

"Yes, Little Mother; No, Little Mother," she would say cheekily.

And whenever her real mother asked her to do anything she would say: "Oh let Mabret do it. I don't want to spoil the Little Mother's fun". But secretly she began to think it was time she had some grown-up jobs too.

One morning Mother had a problem. There were two important jobs to do. Next day was a holy day and the family had friends coming to visit. They had been saving the last of their coffee especially. "I need some extra water and I need some coffee wood," she said.

Fetching water was heavy work. Terhas usually helped with that. Fetching coffee wood was a long job. Mabret usually did that.

Coffee wood came from special trees. It burned slowly and it turned to charcoal as it smouldered. This was just what was needed to keep the coffee simmering for a long time. The trouble with the coffee wood was that you had to walk right over the mountain to find any. It was a long way.

"Mabret will have to help with the water," Mother said. "I will carry the big five gallon plastic container. Mabret can carry the very small one. But who will go for the coffee wood?"

Azmera with her baby brother

"I will," said Azmera, to her mother's surprise. For once Azmera had forgotten to be cheeky, it seemed.

"No," said Mother. "It is too far for your little legs. No, I will have to ask Daniel to go after he has finished helping with the ploughing. You can tell him when you take the breakfast down to the fields," she said to Azmera.

Down in the fields the boys and their father were hard at work. They had risen early and set out as soon as the sun was high enough in the sky to warm the muscles of the oxen. Since then Father and the boys had worked without eating. Only the two oxen had breakfast. They had been given a little of the straw from last year's unripened harvest. It was stored in a small stack behind the house, for such special occasions.

Father was turning over the soil with the oxen yoked to a simple wooden plough. He had borrowed the second ox from a woman whose husband had died. In return Father would plough her land when he had finished his own.

The second ox was called Berhan. He was a younger animal but with a great chest as big as a barrel and a stomach to match. His name meant Light. "But it should be Heavy," joked Azmera when the ox arrived the day before.

Kudos had a better idea. "Look at the size of his stomach. He should be called Belly. Then he would rhyme with the other one. Smelly and Belly," he said.

Azmera liked that. "Belly and Smelly; Smelly and Belly," she said to herself as she approached the two animals which her father was steering over the rocky red soil. With her she carried the bundle her mother had given her. Inside was wrapped four handfuls of roasted wheat grains.

Daniel and Kudos were digging a little dam around the edge of the land. Daniel was swinging a pick-axe. Kudos was moving rocks and boulders with his bare hands. Their plan was to stop water draining away when the rains came. The plain on which they lived was quite flat but it was on the top of a mountain. When it rained all the water just ran away into the valley which dropped steeply at the edge of their land.

At the far end of the field, Father turned the two oxen and ploughed back in a straight line towards the boys. It was heavy work. Father had to lean over to the side all the time as he walked to press the plough's blade down into the soil.

As the two animals reached the spot where the boys were working Kudos bent over to heave an especially big rock. His bottom stuck up in the air just as Senay the ox went past. With a sudden lurch the ox prodded Kudos in the bottom with his horn. Kudos fell flat on his face.

"Owwwww!" cried Kudos. "Who did that?"

"Whoa," shouted Father, pulling the oxen to a halt. "Are you alright?"

Kudos turned to see Senay. "Yes, I'm okay," Kudos said looking right into the eyes of the animal.

Senay stared back. His gaze was blank but it was enough to remind Kudos what had happened at the pool the day before. He rubbed his bottom and wondered if oxen were crafty enough to try to get their own back. But he thought it best not to ask his father.

Father took the little food bundle from Azmera. It was not much breakfast for three people who had been working since dawn. But it was all they were allowed for each meal if the grain was to last until the next sackful came. The grain came from rich countries who sent it to keep people in Eritrea alive until the rains came and crops started to grow again. Father shared out the grain between the four of them.

As they ate they sat and looked at the big mountain behind the village. It ended in a steep cliff which cut through the plain and dropped down one thousand feet to the valley below. Father told Azmera the story that his father had told him when he was a boy. In ancient times, he said, the Archangel Mika'el had promised the people of the village that he would bind the giant cliff with invisible ropes so that not a single stone would ever fall from it.

Azmera looked at the mountain. You had to walk right round it to get to the place where the coffee wood could be found, she knew that. Suddenly an idea popped into her head. She decided not to pass Mother's message on to Daniel.

"Right! Back to work!" said Father and jumped up. The children finished breakfast as they watched him begin to plough again. He shouted "Geddup" to the oxen and his voice bounced from the archangel's rock and echoed round the valley below.

As the oxen ploughed, Azmera moved behind them. Her eyes were fixed upon the new furrows the plough had made in the soil.

She was looking for *kuinte* which were wild seeds which could be found in newly-dug ground. They tasted good and they helped to fill an empty stomach. Whenever she saw one she popped it into the towel. They would keep her going on her secret adventure.

The children finish breakfast as Father starts to plough

At midday it was time to stop work. The sun was high in the sky. It had become too hot for the oxen to continue. They had been ploughing for six hours and were very tired. So were Father and the boys. They all trooped back to the house for a rest.

When they got there they had a pleasant surprise. Mother had made a special lunch of an onion and two eggs served with flat bread.

"Where did you get the eggs?" asked Father.

"I bought them with money I had been saving specially for today. People who have been ploughing need a good lunch," Mother said. She divided the little mound of scrambled eggs and chopped onion into tiny portions and gave everyone a little.

"What about you?" Azmera said to Mother.

"I'm not hungry," Mother lied.

Azmera decided that now was the time for her plan.

"Have my food," she said to her mother. "I had *kuinte* in the field." And before her mother could protest she slipped out of the door.

"What's she up to," said Father, munching away. No-one knew.

For the first hour nobody bothered about where Azmera had gone. Then Mother sent Mabret to a neighbour's house to see if she was there. The family next door were there. But no Azmera.

An hour later Mother wondered again where her youngest daughter could be. She sent Kudos down the hill to the house of Azmera's best friend. All the other girls were there, playing their favourite game with tossing stones. But no Azmera.

Two hours later Mother became really worried. She sent Mabret down to the church. She sent Kudos down to the water pump. She even sent Daniel down to the school across the other side of the main road into town. But no Azmera anywhere.

"This is getting serious," Mother said. "She has been gone for four hours. Soon it will be dark. Azmera has never been away for this long on her own before. When night comes it will be cold and the wild creatures will come out."

Father was worried too. "If she is not back soon I will get the men of the village to go out to search for her."

Just as she spoke there was a noise. Outside the hen squawked. Something had disturbed her as she sat by the gatepost. There was someone in the yard.

"Where shall I put the coffee wood?" said a familiar little voice.

"Azmera!" shouted Mother and rushed outside.

There in the yard stood Azmera with a few more rips in her old green dress. On her head was a battered old tin basin. It was full of the special wood for making coffee.

"Where have you been?" cried Mother. "Are you alright?"

"I've been over the mountain, for the coffee wood," smiled Azmera. "And I'm alright thank you, except that my little legs ache."

Mother gave her a very tight hug.

"Now come inside," Mother said to Azmera," and finish your lunch".

Azmera and her
mother making coffee

CHAPTER THREE

Daniel's midnight journey

"I am not afraid of ghosts," said Daniel to himself. "And I am not afraid of the Monster Monkey." And he threw the old cloth saddle across the donkey's back and set off down the hill.

Everyone in the village was happy. Everyone except Daniel.

They were happy because that day the trucks had arrived from the port. They were full of sacks of wheat which had come from Europe. Now each family would get enough food to last for another month. By then, they all hoped, the rains would have arrived and the crops in the fields would have begun to grow.

But when the food aid arrived it meant a special job for Daniel.

He had to take the family's donkey and go down to the place where the food was given out. It was not far from Daniel's village. But people from other villages came from a long way. Some walked for eight hours and then they had to carry their bags of wheat all the way back.

Some of them had donkeys. But others did not. So whenever it was food day Daniel took the family donkey to help those people carry their food home. In return they gave him a bit of the food or a little money.

Mother liked it best when Daniel got money. Then she could buy a bag of salt or a few eggs.

The problem was that sometimes Daniel had to walk back in the middle of the night. And he had to walk by the big tree which, the Old Woman said, was the home of a ghost. And he had to walk by the waterhole where the Old Man said the Monster Monkey lived.

The Old Man and the Old Woman often chose Daniel to carry their grain. They were from one of the most far off villages. On the journey they told Daniel stories about the places they passed. They were stories they had been told by old people when they were young.

That day, as he trudged down the hill with the donkey, Daniel hoped that he would be able to work for someone else this time. The thought of the old couple's tales haunted him.

As he passed the church, with its fine pink and yellow walls and its green roof, he thought of what his schoolmaster, the priest, would say about such stories.

For three years Daniel had lived away from the village at a school for boys who wanted to be priests. Daniel had not been sure that he wanted to be one. But it had been his father's dearest dream. So he was sent away to live with eleven other boys in the home of a holy man.

He had enjoyed it. In the morning they learned farm work because in Eritrea priests work on the land like everyone else. In the afternoon they learned the alphabet of Ge'ez. This was a language so old that no-one speaks it any more but the prayers of the church in Ethiopia and Eritrea were said in it, as they had been for almost two thousand years. In the evening the boys would learn the prayers.

But two years ago the rains had stopped falling. There had been no

harvest and all their savings had been spent in an earlier drought. Daniel's father could not afford the food and the money which had to be paid to the priest. So Daniel had left the school and returned home. Ten of the eleven boys had done the same.

Daniel still remembered how stern his priest master had been about the stories of the ordinary people. He said they spoke nonsense with their tales of ghosts, spirits and men who could turn themselves in to hyenas. But the old couple just laughed when Daniel once told them what the priest had said.

There were dozens of donkeys and hundreds of people at the place where the food was handed out. Some rushed about. Some pushed and jostled. Some just sat and waited as the people in charge cut open the sacks of wheat and measured out three scoops for each family.

In the middle of them Daniel waited. He looked out for the old couple, hoping not to see them. Just then Kudos appeared.

"What are you doing here?" Daniel asked.

"Mother sent me to find out who you are going with, so we will know when to expect you back," Kudos replied.

It was as if Kudos brought bad luck, as usual. Just as he spoke Daniel felt a tap on his shoulder. He turned to see the Old Man and the Old Woman.

"Tell Mother I'll not be back until tomorrow," he said.

"Watch out for the ghosts and ghoulies," said Kudos with a grin. He rushed off home, with a new piece of mischief already taking shape in his brain. Daniel and the old couple set off.

Opposite: the church doorway

After two hours steady walk up and down the mountain trails they came to a pool. As they approached they disturbed a group of monkeys who were drinking there. The little grey animals squealed loudly and ran away up to the rocks at the top of the mountain.

"Beware this place on the journey home," the Old Man said to Daniel. "This is the pool where at night the Monster Monkey comes to drink. His name is Gawna. If you get between him and the water he will throw huge boulders down upon your head. If you get between him and the prickly pears which grow on the cactus here he will attack you. Beware, he has teeth like daggers to rip your flesh and arms the size of a man's legs to pull you apart."

Daniel looked at the little monkeys as they scampered off up the hill. "What nonsense," he thought to himself. But he said nothing.

After two hours more they came to a ridge. There stood a huge *daaro* tree with tall wild branches. They stopped and leaned against it for a rest.

"Beware this place on the journey home," the Old Woman said to Daniel. "Two travellers stopped here once to rest against the tree and then complained because the tree had no fruit. As they spoke a *zar*, the spirit of the tree, cried out: 'I have given you rest, is that not enough!' And he cursed the two travellers who fell to the ground in a fit. Beware, a *zar* is most powerful at night. It will only keep away if you shout out its name."

Daniel looked at the tree. "What nonsense," he thought to himself. But he said nothing.

After two hours more, as evening was falling, they came to a village. Just outside a blacksmith was fixing a plough. He had made a fire of charcoal in a deep hole in the ground. In it he heated the metal blade of the plough until it became red hot. Then he took it out and beat it with a hammer on a flat stone. The red sparks flew in the darkening light.

"Beware this place on the journey home," the Old Man said to Daniel. "This blacksmith is a *buda*, a spirit of the night who can turn the Evil Eye upon you. Beware, for after dark he can transform himself into a savage hyena."

Daniel looked at the blacksmith. "What nonsense," he thought to himself. But he said nothing.

Darkness fell just before they reached the old couple's village two hours later. Daniel unloaded the donkey and gratefully took the money they paid him. He set off on the long lonely journey home, driving the weary donkey before him. Above him he could see thousands of tiny stars winking like the lights of a far off town.

Just before midnight the moon came out. Sometimes in Africa the moon looks huge. It hangs low in the sky and lights up the whole desert with a soft grey shine. But this moon was a small one and high in the sky. Daniel could only just pick out the vague outline of the houses as he reached the village of the blacksmith.

All was quiet. Everyone was asleep. Only the glowing embers of the blacksmith's fire remained.

"I don't believe in nonsense about men turning into hyenas," Daniel suddenly said out loud, as if he was talking to the donkey. "But we had best keep an eye out for real hyenas. For the jaws of a spotted hyena can crack the thigh-bone of an ox."

He walked on, straining his ears for the mad cackle or the wailing

The old man who told Daniel about the Master Monkey

Opposite: Daniel wrapped against the cold night air

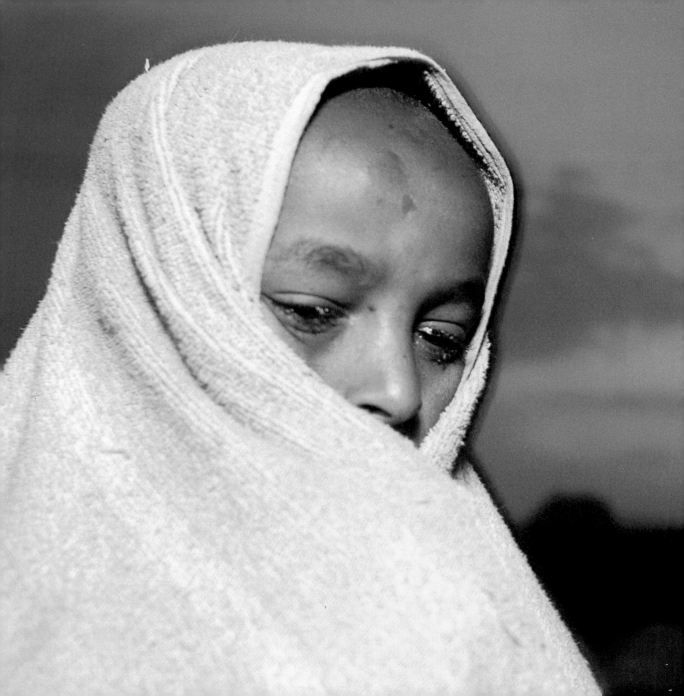

whoop of a hyena. But there was nothing to break the silence of the night.

Two hours later he reached the ridge. The huge *daaro* tree stood outlined against the moon with its wild branches waving like clawing fingers in the night wind. It was getting cold. Daniel shivered and pulled his blanket tightly around him.

"I don't believe in nonsense about spirits which live in trees," thought Daniel. But he kept well clear of the great tree. And to give himself courage he shouted, in his loudest voice: "I am not afraid of the Zar of the Daaro!"

And he walked on, straining his ears for the yowling howl of the tree spirit. But there was nothing to break the silence of the night.

Two hours later he reached the pool where the monkeys had been drinking. It was meant to be the home of Gawna, the Monster Monkey with teeth like daggers and arms the size of a man's legs.

"I don't believe in nonsense about the Monster Monkey," said Daniel to the donkey.

But he had seen the small monkeys there himself. And he knew that big baboons had lived among these rocks before the drought came. His uncle had told him of how the men once came to hunt them with dogs. He had told how they could kill a dog easily with their long jaws and huge front teeth which were one-and-a-half inches long. He had told how mad they could get if you picked their prickly pears. He had spoken of how they had rolled boulders down from the mountain top to injure the hunters. Perhaps Gawna really did exist.

Daniel walked on, straining his ears for the fierce screech of an angry baboon. But there was nothing to break the silence of the night.

Dawn was beginning to break. There was lightness in the sky. Soon the first rays of the sun would appear over the long back of the mountain ahead of him. Home was only on the other side.

Suddenly a wild shriek cut through the air. Daniel's heart seemed to stop. The blood in his arms and legs went suddenly cold. In the growing light he could see a strange shape among the rocks in front of him. It was dark and furry.

Suddenly it spoke in a strange and croaky voice. "Who dares to come to the pool of the Monster Monkey?" it said.

Daniel stood fixed to the spot. Then, stooping down he picked up a big stone and hurled it. Thud! It hit the furry shape on the back and bounced off.

"Owwww!" said the furry shape, in a very different and rather familiar voice. "Stop, it's me"

The shape stood up and pulled the goatskin from off its head. Underneath was Kudos, the Mischief Boy.

"You beast!" Kudos said. "Mother sent me to meet you with some breakfast and walk back with you. And this is all the thanks I get. I'll have a big bruise on my back now."

"That'll teach you," said Daniel, laughing with relief. "I knew it was you all along, of course."

Kudos was not so sure but he rubbed his back and decided it would be best not to disagree.

CHAPTER FOUR

The dozy donkey disaster

Kudos touched his toes and stuck his bottom in the air. His pants were round his ankles. And his mother was slowly, and painfully, pulling cactus thorns out one by one. It had been one of those days.

It had all begun in an ordinary enough way. That morning, nearly a month after Daniel's midnight journey, Father had called the family together to plan the day.

"Right," he said. "Today I am going to an important meeting which will decide on what land we have to farm next year."

In their village the land was divided up into areas known as *tsemdi*. A *tsemdi* was the amount of land which one man could plough with two oxen in a single day. Every seven years each family was given a different piece of land. It was all decided at a meeting where some-one from each family drew a piece of paper from a bowl which had the name of one *tsemdi* on it. This way everyone would get the chance to have the good land from time to time.

"I will be away all day because first we have to discuss how to divide the land. Then we have to draw the lots," said Father, "So I want to make sure that you all know what your jobs are for the day."

Daniel was to cut cactus and burn the thorns off it for the ox's dinner. Kudos was to take the donkey to their grandfather who owned the animal and needed it back for a few days. Mabret was to help her mother fetch water. Azmera was to gather firewood for the stove from the nearest hillside.

"To work!" shouted Father.

Kudos went over to the low stable in the corner of the yard to get the donkey.

"Come on dozy donkey," he said.

The animal turned its head towards the wall and took no notice.

"Dumb, dozy donkey," said Kudos. And he poked it with his stick.

The donkey turned round and gave him a withering look. Then it turned away again. It was ignoring him.

"Dopey, dumb, dozy donkey," said Kudos, who was in no mood to be ignored. He gave it a mighty prod in the backside.

The donkey revolved slowly around and took four steps out into the middle of the yard. Then it stopped again. That was as far as it intended to go.

"Dim, dopey, dumb, dozy donkey," said Kudos. And he gave it a whack across the back with his stick. At least he meant it to be across the back. But just at the last moment the donkey stepped backwards. The stick hit it right across the neck.

All at once, to Kudos's horror, the donkey's legs collapsed under it. It fell in a heap on the floor. Then it rolled over onto its side and lay still.

Kudos stood with his mouth wide open.

Inside the house his parents heard the sudden commotion and came rushing out.

"What happened?" Father shouted.

"I just hit him, and he fell over," said Kudos.

Father looked with wild eyes at the donkey. It wasn't even his. How would he get the money to buy another for his father-in-law?

"I didn't hit him hard," said Kudos. "I wasn't even holding my stick at the end – just in the middle."

The donkey was not strong, Father knew that. You could see its hip bones sticking out through its dry wiry skin. There was no good grass anywhere for it to eat.

"Where did you hit him?"

"On the neck."

"You stupid boy. Hit on the rump, never on the neck," said Father. "Spit on the blow. Spit on it."

Kudos knew what his father was talking about. In his country if you insulted someone you could take back the insult by spitting. It was not considered bad manners. A blow could be taken back in the same way.

But the Mischief Boy thought that it was funny to do it to a donkey. He laughed nervously.

"Don't smirk, boy. This is serious," Father said. And he fetched him a great wallop around the ear. Kudos began to cry and to spit, both at the same time.

Father turned to his wife and shouted: "The ashes of Abune Aregawe. . . quick."

Mother snatched a small bottle hanging by the door. It contained the ashes of some holy relic. They had been blessed by a priest at the shrine of Aregawe, an Ethiopian saint who, it was said, had been lifted

Daniel in
the cactus patch

up to God on the tail of a dragon. She sprinkled a little in a basin and filled it with water.

Father took the bowl and placed it by the famished donkey's head. He flicked the water onto the animal's tongue. The donkey licked its lips. Then it opened its eyes, saw the water and began to drink.

"I didn't hit him very hard," said Kudos. "It was only a tap. He's just weak from hunger."

The donkey shook its head like a dog drying itself when it comes out of a river. Then it stood up, shakily.

"Abune Aregawe has saved him. God is with us," said Father. "Daniel, you look after the poor animal. Let this blessed nuisance cut the cactus."

Daniel stopped work in the cactus patch. He came back to the yard and passed the big knife over to Kudos. Then he went to look after the donkey. Kudos went off silently to cut the big fat cactus leaves. His name, in their language, meant Blessed. For his father to call him Blessed Nuisance he had to be very cross indeed.

The cactus grew wild. But because it was useful food for the cattle most families cultivated their own patch. Kudos stood in the middle of the patch on the steep hillside next to their house and looked around. Daniel shouted some advice.

"Don't cut the ones with flowers on, because they will turn into delicious prickly pears. Don't cut the very big ones because that is where next year's leaves will grow. Cut the middle sized ones," he said.

"I know, I know," said Kudos, grumpily, without looking up.

"And be careful of the thorns," warned Daniel. "The thorns on the big ones are sharp. But the thorns on the small ones are worst. They feel just like prickles. But if they prick you they work their way under your skin and won't come out for a long time. They will give you a terrible rash."

"I'm not stupid, you know," said Kudos, standing up fiercely to glare at his brother. As he did so his feet slipped on the loose stones. And he fell back and sat on a big cactus.

And that was how Kudos came to be stood there with his bare bottom in the air while Mother pulled the big thorns out of the flesh. She cleaned her teeth as she worked, chewing on a twig of olive wood which is what everyone uses for a toothbrush in the highlands.

"That's not a pretty sight," said a familiar voice.

Kudos stayed bent over but moved his head to see who was there. Mother turned too.

"Terhas!" she shouted. It was her eldest daughter, back from the holy spring she had visited to cure her dizzy fits.

Mother and Terhas stepped towards each other. Mother held out her face and Terhas kissed her eight times, with four kisses on each cheek. Then she gave a little bow. This was the proper way to greet your mother after a long absence in Eritrea.

"We thought you'd be back a couple of days ago," Mother said.

"It took longer than I thought. But I feel fine now. And there was a delay on the way back. The road was washed away by floods."

"It's a pity that none of the rain fell here," Mother said. "We have had none at all."

They looked set for a full-scale gossip when a very-sorry-for-itself little voice said: "Hey, what about me?".

They turned to see Kudos, still with his bottom in the air, but with his head swivelled round towards them. He looked like an ostrich with its head stuck in the sand. Mother and Terhas burst out laughing.

"Okay," said Mother to Terhas. "Let me finish Little Thorn-bum here and then we'll have a proper chat."

"Mum!" said Kudos. "Don't say Bum, it's rude."

Mother said nothing, but pulled out another thorn in reply.

"Owwwww!" said the Mischief Boy.

Terhas picked up the baby and held him in the air with his legs wriggling. "Ma-ma-ma-ma-ma-ma-mouche," she sang. Mamouche was the word for Baby Boy.

"Tonight we will have a feast," she said. "I got a little work helping parcel up the food aid for distribution in the town on the way back. I have brought some goodies."

That night the whole family was back together for the splendid evening meal. Terhas had brought wheat, so Mother made *himbasha*, a special bread which was dark and strong and tasted like gingerbread. And there were tomatoes, onions, green peppers, eggs, coffee, sugar and salt – all from the stout bag Terhas had brought with her.

Father took the bread in his hands and blessed and broke it.

They all said: "Amen". And then they tucked in.